Developing process safety indicators

A step-by-step guide for chemical and major hazard industries

HSE Books

Contents

Foreword

There is a collective need for the chemical and major hazard sectors to demonstrate that risks are being adequately controlled, as the industry is often judged by the worst performer or against the last major incident to gain public attention. Since the publication of the *BP Grangemouth Major incident investigation report*,[1] the Health and Safety Executive (HSE) and industry have been working closely to develop the means by which companies can develop key performance indicators for major hazards and ensure process safety performance is monitored and reported against these parameters.

This guide has been produced jointly by HSE and the Chemical Industries Association (CIA), based on information and ideas from industry. The six-stage process outlined should help companies through the main steps towards implementing process safety performance indicators.

Investigation of major incidents chemical and major hazard installations have shown that it is vital that chemical companies know that systems designed to control risks operate as intended. This work, built from close collaboration between HSE and industry, helps provide this assurance. It is important that we continue to share understanding of best practice in this developing area. Reviewing performance will increasingly feature in our inspection programme.

Our Responsible Care®[2] commitment is to continuous improvement in all aspects of health, safety and environmental management. This important new initiative will help us all gain a better understanding of potentially serious incident precursors, and will enable us to make further improvements to our overall health, safety and environmental management systems.

Steve Elliot
Director General Chemical Industries Association

Kevin Allars
Head of Chemical Industries Division
HSE

Part 1: Introduction

> *Measurement leads to confidence.*

1   This guide is intended for senior managers and safety professionals within organisations that wish to develop performance indicators to provide assurance that major hazard risks are under control. A small number of carefully chosen indicators can monitor the status of key systems and provide an early warning should controls deteriorate dangerously.

2   Although primarily aimed at major hazard organisations, the generic model for establishing a performance measurement system described in this guide can equally be applied to other enterprises requiring a high level of assurance that systems and procedures continue to operate as intended.

3   It is presumed that companies using this guide already have appropriate safety management systems in place; the emphasis of this guide is therefore to check whether the controls in place are effective and operating as intended.

4   Too many organisations rely heavily on failure data to monitor performance. The consequence of this approach is that improvements or changes are only determined after something has gone wrong. Often the difference between whether a system failure results in a minor or a catastrophic outcome is purely down to chance. Effective management of major hazards requires a proactive approach to risk management, so information to confirm critical systems are operating as intended is essential. Switching the emphasis in favour of leading indicators to confirm that risk controls continue to operate is an important step forward in the management of major hazard risks.

5   The main reason for measuring process safety performance is to provide ongoing assurance that risks are being adequately controlled. Directors and senior managers need to monitor the effectiveness of internal controls against business risks. For major hazard installations and chemical manufacturers, process safety risks will be a significant aspect of business risk, asset integrity and reputation. Many organisations do not have good information to show how well they are managing major hazard risks. This is because the information gathered tends to be limited to measuring failures, such as incidents or near misses. Discovering weaknesses in control systems by having a major incident is too late and too costly. Early warning of dangerous deterioration within critical systems

provides an opportunity to avoid major incidents. Knowing that process risks are effectively controlled has a clear link with business efficiency, as several indicators can be used to show plant availability and optimised operating conditions.

6   The method of setting indicators outlined in this guide requires those involved in managing process safety risks to ask some fundamental questions about their systems, such as:

- What can go wrong?
- What controls are in place to prevent major incidents?
- What does each control deliver in terms of a **'safety outcome'**?
- How do we know they continue to operate as intended?

7   Companies who have adopted process safety performance indicators have reported that they have:

- an increased assurance on risk management and protected reputation;
- demonstrated the suitability of their risk control systems;
- avoided discovering weaknesses through costly incidents;
- stopped collecting and reporting performance information which was no longer relevant – thereby saving costs; and
- made better use of information already collected for other purposes, eg quality management.

Structure and content

8   **Part 2**, the main part of this guide, describes a six-step process that can be adopted by organisations wishing to implement a programme of performance measurement for process safety risks. Each stage is explained in detail within a separate chapter. To help put the process into context, a full worked example for a top-tier COMAH[3] site is included in **Part 3**.

9   Although this model can be followed step-by-step, many organisations already have a performance measurement system in place and may not wish to embark on radical change. In such circumstances, this guide may be used as a framework against which to compare existing programmes to decide if improvements are needed, as it draws on good practice within the UK chemical sector.

10 Throughout this guide, the term **'process safety management system'** is used to describe those parts of an organisation's management system intended to prevent major incidents arising out of the production, storage and handling of dangerous substances. **'Risk control system'** (RCS) is used to describe a constituent part of a process safety management system that focuses on a specific risk or activity, eg plant and process change, permit to work, inspection and maintenance etc.

Measuring performance – early warning before catastrophic failure

11 Most systems and procedures deteriorate over time, and system failures discovered following a major incident frequently surprise senior managers, who sincerely believed that the controls were functioning as designed. Used effectively, process safety indicators can provide an early warning, before catastrophic failure, that critical controls have deteriorated to an unacceptable level.

12 Measuring performance to assess how effectively risks are being controlled is an essential part of a health and safety management system, as explained in *Successful health and safety management*,[4] and, for example, the CIA's *Responsible Care Management Systems*:[5]

- **active monitoring** provides feedback on performance before an accident or incident; whereas
- **reactive monitoring** involves identifying and reporting on incidents to check the controls in place are adequate, to identify weaknesses or gaps in control systems and to learn from mistakes.

What's different about this guide?

Dual assurance – a leading and lagging indicator for each risk control system

13 The main difference between the approach outlined in this guide and existing guidance on performance measurement is the introduction of the concept of 'dual assurance' that key risk control systems are operating as intended. Leading and lagging indicators are set in a structured and systematic way for each critical risk control system within the whole process safety management system. In tandem they act as system guardians providing dual assurance to confirm that the risk control system is operating as intended or providing a warning that problems are starting to develop.

Leading indicators

14 Leading indicators are a form of active monitoring focused on a few critical risk control systems to ensure their continued effectiveness. **Leading indicators require a routine systematic check that key actions or activities are undertaken as intended.** They can be considered as measures of process or inputs essential to deliver the desired safety outcome.

Lagging indicators

15 Lagging indicators are a form of reactive monitoring requiring the reporting and investigation of specific incidents and events to discover weaknesses in that system. These incidents or events do not have to result in major damage or injury or even a loss of containment, providing that they represent a failure of a significant control system which guards against or limits the consequences of a major incident. **Lagging indicators show when a desired safety outcome has failed, or has not been achieved.**

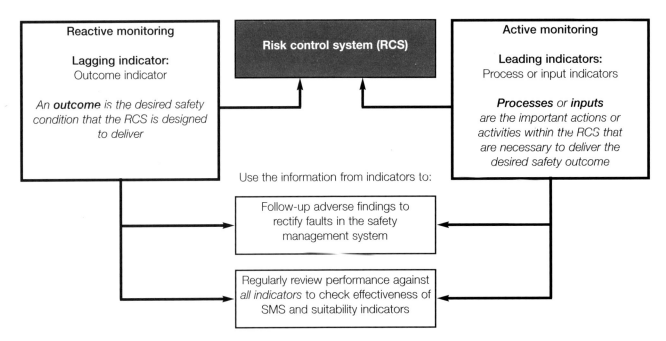

Figure 1 Dual assurance – leading and lagging indicators measuring performance of each critical risk control system

16   According to James Reason in *Managing the Risks of Organizational Accidents*,[6] (major) accidents result when a series of failings within several critical risk control systems materialise concurrently. Figure 2 illustrates an 'accident trajectory' model where an accident trajectory passes through corresponding holes in the layers of defence, barriers and safeguards. Each risk control system represents an important barrier or safeguard within the process safety management system. It should also be recognised that a significant failing in just one critical barrier may be sufficient in itself to give rise to a major accident.

17   For each risk control system:

■   the leading indicator identifies failings or 'holes' in vital aspects of the risk control system discovered **during routine checks** on the operation of a critical activity within the risk control system; and

■   the lagging indicator reveals failings or 'holes' in that barrier discovered **following an incident or adverse event.** The incident does not necessarily have to result in injury or environmental damage and can be a near miss, precursor event or undesired outcome attributable to a failing in that risk control system.

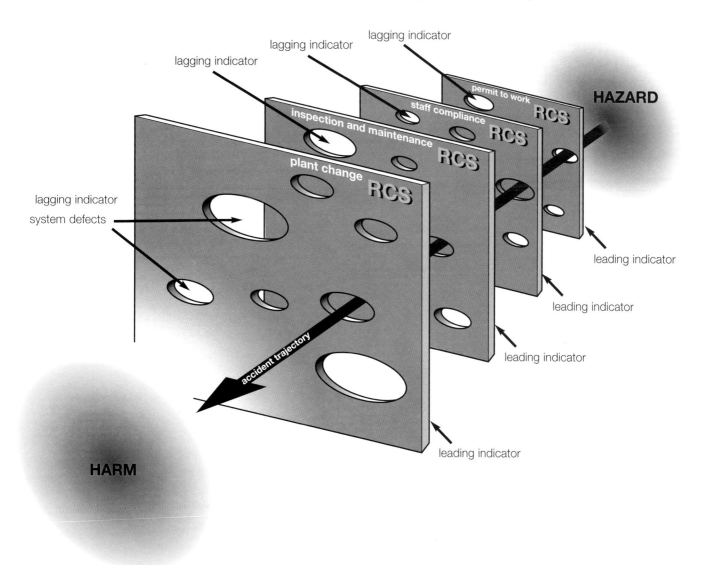

Figure 2   Leading and lagging indicators set to detect defects in important risk control systems

(Reproduced with permission of Ashgate Publishing Limited, from *Managing the Risks of Organizational Accidents* James Reason 1997 Ashgate Publishing Limited)[6]

18 If unchecked, all systems will deteriorate over time and major incidents occur when defects across a number of risk control systems materialise concurrently. Setting leading and lagging indicators for each risk critical control system should reveal failings in these barriers as they arise and before all the important barriers are defeated.

Frequency of checks

19 Many organisations rely on auditing to highlight system deterioration. However, audit intervals can be too infrequent to detect rapid change, or the audit may focus on compliance (verifying the right systems are in place), rather than ensuring systems are delivering the desired safety outcome. The use of process safety performance indicators fits between these formal, infrequent audits and more frequent workplace inspection and safety observation programmes. It is important to bear in mind that an audit programme may be designed to address different issues when compared to the information gained from performance indicators. Ideally, each will inform the other. Deficiencies uncovered by an audit may highlight the need for a new performance indicator and vice versa. Therefore, performance indicators are not a substitute for an audit programme but a complimentary activity to give more frequent or different information on system performance.

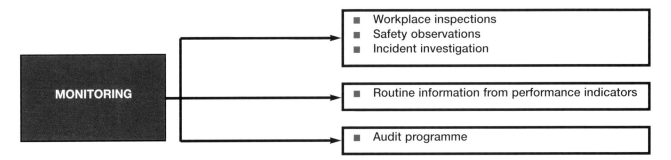

Figure 3 How performance indicators fit within normal health and safety monitoring activities

Part 2: Six steps to performance measurement

20 This section outlines the six main stages needed to implement a process safety measurement system. Organisations that do not have a process safety performance measurement system would benefit from considering each stage in turn. Organisations with performance measurement systems in place can use this guide as a benchmark of good practice and consider improvements as appropriate.

Table 1 Overview of the six steps to setting performance indicators

Step 1	Establish the organisational arrangements to implement the indicators	Appoint a steward or champion
		Set up an implementation team
		Senior management should be involved
Step 2	Decide on the scope of the measurement system. Consider what can go wrong and where	Select the organisational level
		Identify the scope of the measurement system: ■ Identify incident scenarios – what can go wrong? ■ Identify the immediate causes of hazard scenarios ■ Review performance and non-conformances
Step 3	Identify the risk control systems in place to prevent a major accidents. Decide on the outcomes for each and **set a lagging indicator**	What risk control systems are in place?
		Describe the outcome
		Set a lagging indicator
		Follow up deviations from the outcome
Step 4	Identify the critical elements of each risk control system, (ie those actions or processes which must function correctly to deliver the outcomes) and **set leading indicators**	What are the most important parts of the risk control system?
		Set leading indicators
		Set tolerances
		Follow up deviations from tolerances
Step 5	Establish the data collection and reporting system	Collect information – ensure information/unit of measurement is available or can be established
		Decide on presentation format
Step 6	Review	Review performance of process management system
		Review the scope of the indicators
		Review the tolerances

Step 1: Establish the organisational arrangements to implement indicators

> ■ **Appoint a steward or champion to take the initiative forward.**
>
> ■ **In larger organisations, consider using a process safety steering committee.**
>
> ■ **Senior management should be actively involved in the development of indicators.**

21 New organisational arrangements may be needed to implement a performance measurement system. Someone will have to make the case for process safety measurement within the company and then drive it forward to implementation. The benefits and the costs will need to be carefully considered and the details of the exact indicators determined.

Step 1.1: Appoint a steward or champion

22 A steward or champion is needed to:

■ promote, drive forward and co-ordinate the introduction of the new concept and system;
■ make the business case and link with company health, safety, environment, quality and business improvement systems;
■ communicate ideas and progress;
■ keep in touch with others working in this area and gather information on best practice; and
■ identify and evaluate the benefits achieved.

Make the business case

23 Developing and implementing process safety indicators is often a new area of work within many organisations, and the need for such a system will not be immediately obvious to many people. To be successful, this sort of initiative requires someone within the organisation to promote the idea, gauge support and then to drive forward the initiative. This may include making the business case for adopting performance indicators and securing suitable resources.

24 Monitoring and measuring performance has always been part of health and safety management systems. However, such systems frequently overlook process safety issues because it is difficult to know what to measure and how to set leading indicators. Where performance indicators already feature in a company health and safety management system, it is important for someone to check the suitability of those indicators for providing ongoing assurance on the control of process safety risks. It could be that existing performance

indicators may only show half the story and that dual assurance derived from selecting a leading and lagging indicator for each critical RCS can add significantly to such a system. Clarifying gaps and weaknesses in existing measurement systems and identifying the associated business risks will be a key part of any case for change.

Identifying the business benefits

25 Identifying associated business benefits that can accrue from improved process safety measurement (such as improved productivity, efficiency, reduction in the cost of loss-of-containment incidents and improved asset management) will help to sell the initiative within the organisation.

Learning from others and sharing good practice

26 This is a developing area of work with new ideas and experiences of using process safety indicators emerging all the time. To avoid starting with a blank sheet of paper, it is helpful to know what others within the industry are doing and what represents good practice. It is important therefore that someone keeps up to date with these developments, eg by joining HSE's web community forum[7] or participating in a CIA *Responsible Care Cell*.[8]

Step 1.2: Set up an implementation team

27 Consider the following factors to decide whether an implementation team is needed:

■ the workload may be too much work for one person;
■ there may be extra benefit from a team approach – eg collective ideas;
■ large organisations with busy safety committees may need a separate forum/steering committee;
■ involving employees should foster a shared understanding and ownership of risks and controls.

28 It will usually be a safety professional within an organisation who will champion the work and steer it through to implementation. However, in large organisations there will be too much for one person to deal with alone and it is often more appropriate to form a team to manage the introduction of process safety indicators. This has the benefit of drawing in people from a range of business operations, providing the opportunity for pooling ideas, especially from employees who have direct knowledge of how systems deteriorate or become ineffective. A steering committee may also be helpful to oversee the implementation programme and to check the indicators

match current business priorities. For top-tier COMAH sites, the implementation team and steering group (where used) should comprise of people familiar with the safety report.

Step 1.3: Senior management involvement

- Directors and senior managers are the main customers for risk assurance information.

- Senior managers should actively participate in the implementation.

- Business benefits should be agreed.

29   The active control of business risks by directors and senior managers is an essential part of corporate governance.[9] Senior managers need to fully understand the business benefits of performance measurement and clearly see how managing process safety contributes to the success and sustainability of their company. It is vital that senior managers are committed to adopting meaningful indicators as they have ultimate responsibility for the control of risk and are therefore the main customer for the enhanced information. It is important that management teams, chief executives and directors agree that the indicators chosen provide them with the right scope and level of information they need to be satisfied that process safety risks are under control.

30   Senior managers need to make appropriate resources and support available for the introduction of process safety indicators.

Step 2: Decide on the scope of the indicators

Select the organisational level to which indicators will apply, eg:

■ **the whole organisation;**

■ **an individual site or group of sites;**

■ **an individual installation/plant.**

31 Setting the scope is about selecting the right indicators to provide just enough information about the adequacy of process safety controls. Performance can be monitored at a number of organisational levels within a business and the information can be presented in a hierarchical manner. The nature of the indicators will vary depending upon the organisational level at which they have been set. Indicators set for the whole organisational will, by their nature, tend to be more generic, whereas those set at plant or site level will be more focused on key activities or processes and give more direct feedback on the functioning of those activities.

Tailor the indicators to suit the business

32 The management systems and activities of every organisation are different and so the way performance indicators may be used will also differ from one organisation to another. There is no right system to suit every need and many enterprises already have key performance indicators (KPIs) covering a number of business activities. It is important that new indicators covering process safety are integrated into and complement existing arrangements for monitoring business performance.

How many indicators? Quality not quantity

33 It is not necessary to measure every aspect or element of a process safety management system. Focusing on a few critical risk control systems will provide a sufficient overview of performance. Problems highlighted in one risk control system should trigger a more widespread review.

34 Busy management teams will quickly lose interest in an extensive raft of indicators, so it is essential to avoid KPI overload. Data collection and analysis is resource intensive, so arrangements for monitoring performance have to be cost effective. Even for the largest organisations a few indicators set against the main risks will be sufficient to

provide a high degree of assurance across the whole business.

Step 2.1: Select the organisational level

35 This section applies mainly to large or multi-site organisations.

Decide whether to set indicators at organisation, site or installation/plant level.

36 Many large organisations cascade performance targets downwards through the management chain and require performance information against such targets to be reported back upwards. Traditionally, upward reporting comprised simply of exceptional reporting of incidents. To provide assurance, information to confirm that key systems are operating as intended should be routinely reported upwards to directors and senior managers.

37 Indicators set at plant level provide managers with routine information to show that specific processes or activities are operating as intended, eg plant design, plant change, planned inspection and maintenance within that sphere of operations. Indicators at this level provide very specific performance information on the activities selected.

38 Indicators at site level provide an overview of critical systems operating across the whole site. Using a hierarchical approach, information from individual installations or operational plants can be summarised across the whole site, eg managing contractors, emergency arrangements, staff competence.

39 At an organisational level, a short summary of high-level indicators is needed. These may be based on corporate goals and objectives (a top-down approach), but importantly, should also feature information fed up from site level.

40 For complex sites such as refineries and within multi-site organisations, the performance measurement system can be based on a hierarchical approach with very focused installation level indicators feeding up to more generic site level and organisation level indicators. Low level indicators can be weighted to reflect their importance at a particular site or installation, or can be designated as 'index indicators' to show that the most impact systems are operating as intended across the site or organisation.

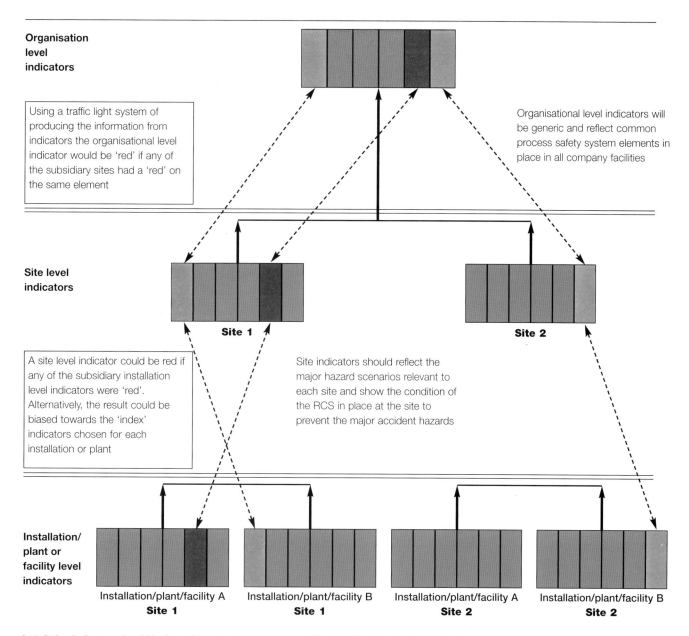

Organisation level indicators

Using a traffic light system of producing the information from indicators the organisational level indicator would be 'red' if any of the subsidiary sites had a 'red' on the same element

Organisational level indicators will be generic and reflect common process safety system elements in place in all company facilities

Site level indicators

Site 1

Site 2

A site level indicator could be red if any of the subsidiary installation level indicators were 'red'. Alternatively, the result could be biased towards the 'index' indicators chosen for each installation or plant

Site indicators should reflect the major hazard scenarios relevant to each site and show the condition of the RCS in place at the site to prevent the major accident hazards

Installation/ plant or facility level indicators

Installation/plant/facility A
Site 1

Installation/plant/facility B
Site 1

Installation/plant/facility A
Site 2

Installation/plant/facility B
Site 2

Installation indicators should be based on what can go wrong at the individual installation to give rise to a major accident/serious incident. Installation level indicators should be very focused on the individual RCS critical to the safe operation of that installation or plant

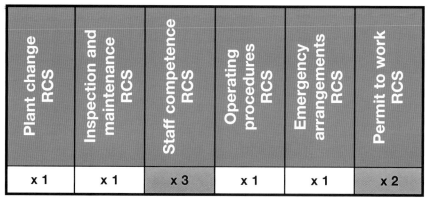

Plant change RCS	Inspection and maintenance RCS	Staff competence RCS	Operating procedures RCS	Emergency arrangements RCS	Permit to work RCS
x 1	x 1	x 3	x 1	x 1	x 2

Individual RCS may be given different weightings based upon the criticality of that RCS for the installation/plant, eg staff competence and permit to work may be the most critical or vulnerable RCS on Installation A, whereas inspection and maintenance may be the most important RCS at Installation B, etc. These higher weighted RCS could then be used as 'index' indicators for the whole site

Installation/plant/facility A

Figure 4 A hierarchical Process Safety Performance Management System for a multi-site organisation

Dual assurance

41   Figure 5 illustrates the method used to establish firstly a lagging indicator and then leading indicators for each important risk control system. The strong link between leading and lagging indicators acting in tandem provides dual assurance that the risk in question is being effectively managed.

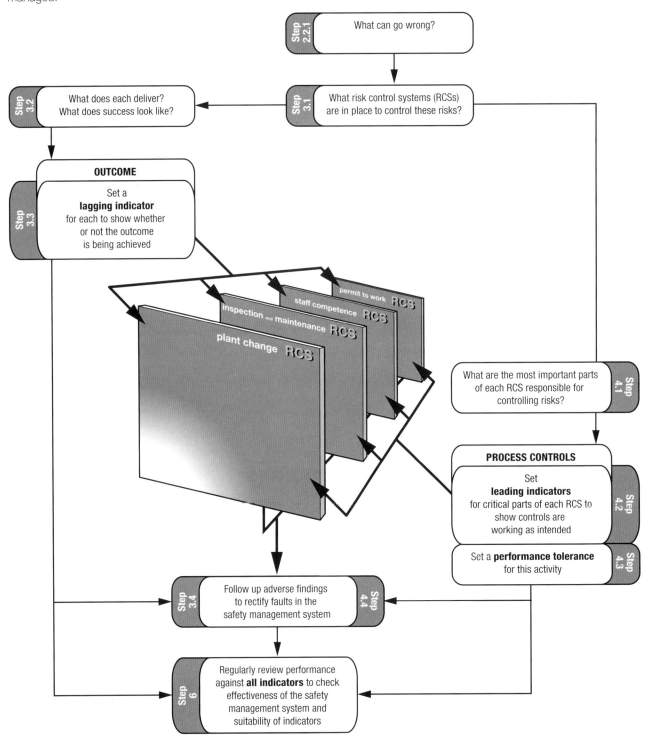

Figure 5 Setting indicators - an overview

Step 2.2: Identify the scope of the measurement system

Identify the scope based on:

- **the main process safety risks and key risk control systems;**

- **areas where greater assurance on business risk is needed.**

2.2.1: Identify hazard scenarios – what can go wrong?

42 It is important to set leading and lagging indicators for the important risk control systems in place to control or mitigate against major hazards – see Figures 1 and 2. These will differ depending upon where in the organisation it is decided to set the indicators.

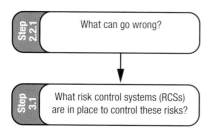

Figure 6 Identify what can go wrong

43 For COMAH[3] top-tier installations, the risk control systems will have been fully described in the safety report. At COMAH lower tier installations and other sites, identify the process safety risks by first identifying a range of hazard scenarios associated with the business or activity being considered, eg how major accidents and incidents can occur from activities such as storage, use and transfer of hazardous substances. Ask what can go wrong within each main area of your business.

44 Describing the main incident scenarios helps you focus on the most important activities and controls against which indicators should be set. The scenarios form a useful cross-check later on in Step 4, when the critical elements of risk control systems to be monitored are determined.

2.2.2: Identify the immediate causes of hazard scenarios

45 To help decide what can go wrong and how, it is useful to consider the immediate cause of an incident. This is the primary failure mechanism that gives rise to an incident and can usually be categorised by conditions or factors that **challenge** the integrity of plant or equipment. For instance, a pipeline or bulk tank failure could be due to:

- wear;
- corrosion;
- damage;
- over/under pressurisation; or
- fire or explosion.

46 Look also at areas where there are known problems or concerns about the adequacy of risk control systems. This could be based on past incident/near-miss data or information from audits and inspections. It is beneficial to include workforce representatives in this process, as it will address issues of most concern to them.

47 An assessment of all these factors should help establish the scope of the process measurement system and ensure you focus on critical issues.

Step 3: Identify the risk control systems and decide on the outcomes

- List the important risk control systems.

- Describe the outcome for each risk control system.

- Set a lagging indicator to show whether the outcome is achieved.

If you don't clearly identify the 'desired safety outcome' in terms of 'success', it will be impossible to identify indicators that show the desired outcome is being achieved.

Step 3.1: What risk control systems are in place?

48 For each scenario identify the risk control systems in place to prevent or mitigate the consequences of these events. There may be several interrelated or overlapping risk control systems aimed at prevention or mitigation. It may be helpful to draw up a risk control system matrix as illustrated in **Part 3**, Table 3.

Identify the primary cause

49 To determine which risk control systems are important to prevent or control a challenge to integrity, first consider the primary causes of the scenarios identified in Step 2.2.2. For example, the primary causes of plant or equipment **wear** could be:

- physical abrasion;
- vibration; or
- stress.

50 A planned plant inspection and maintenance system is a key risk control system expected to be in place to prevent plant failure due to **wear**.

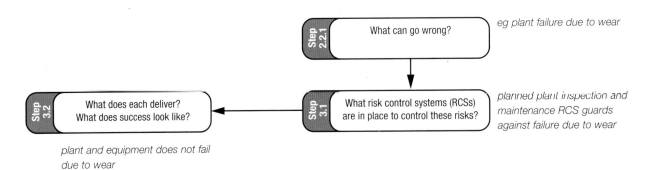

Figure 7 Consider what risk control systems are in place

Step 3.2: Describe the outcome

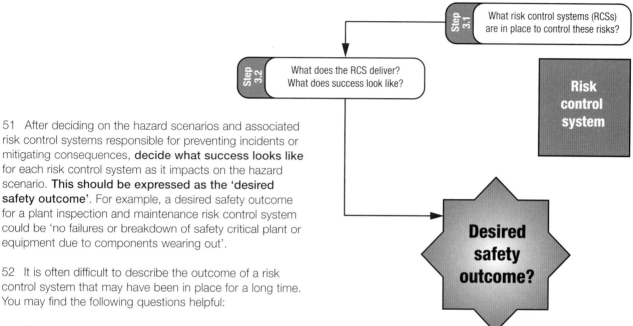

51   After deciding on the hazard scenarios and associated risk control systems responsible for preventing incidents or mitigating consequences, **decide what success looks like** for each risk control system as it impacts on the hazard scenario. **This should be expressed as the 'desired safety outcome'.** For example, a desired safety outcome for a plant inspection and maintenance risk control system could be 'no failures or breakdown of safety critical plant or equipment due to components wearing out'.

52   It is often difficult to describe the outcome of a risk control system that may have been in place for a long time. You may find the following questions helpful:

■ Why do we have this risk control system?
■ What does it deliver in terms of safety?
■ What would be the consequence if we didn't have this system in place?

Figure 8 Describe the desired safety outcome

Step 3.3: Setting a lagging indicator

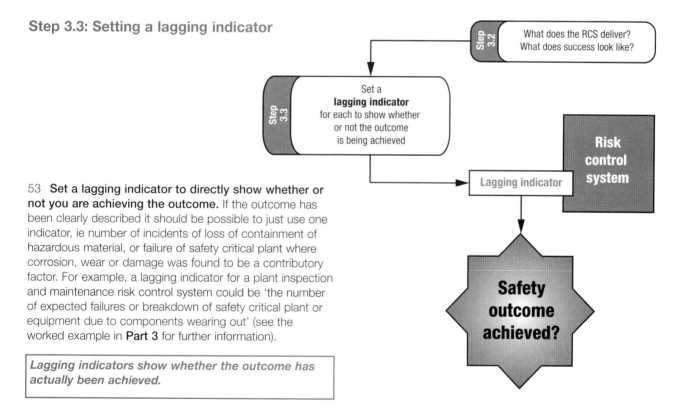

53   **Set a lagging indicator to directly show whether or not you are achieving the outcome.** If the outcome has been clearly described it should be possible to just use one indicator, ie number of incidents of loss of containment of hazardous material, or failure of safety critical plant where corrosion, wear or damage was found to be a contributory factor. For example, a lagging indicator for a plant inspection and maintenance risk control system could be 'the number of expected failures or breakdown of safety critical plant or equipment due to components wearing out' (see the worked example in **Part 3** for further information).

> *Lagging indicators show whether the outcome has actually been achieved.*

Figure 9 Set a lagging indicator to show whether or not the outcome is achieved

Step 3.4: Follow up deviations from the outcome

54 Setting indicators will not lead to improved performance unless every deviation from the intended outcome or failure of a critical part of a risk control system is followed up. For lagging indicators, every time the outcome is not achieved there should be an investigation to see why the system failed. Each occasion provides an opportunity to consider whether improvements should be made. Lessons from these enquiries should be applied across the whole organisation.

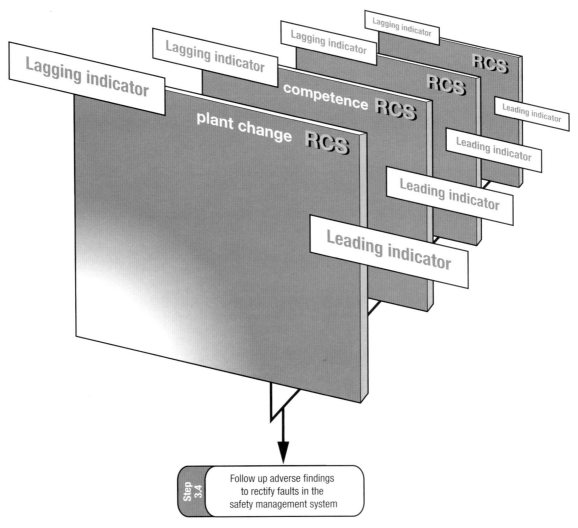

Figure 10 Follow up adverse findings

Step 4: Identify critical elements of each risk control system

> ■ **Identify elements of each risk control system that are vital to deliver the outcome.**
>
> ■ **Set leading indicators to monitor effectiveness of those elements of the risk control system.**
>
> ■ **Set the range of tolerance for each indicator.**

Step 4.1: What are the most important parts of the risk control system?

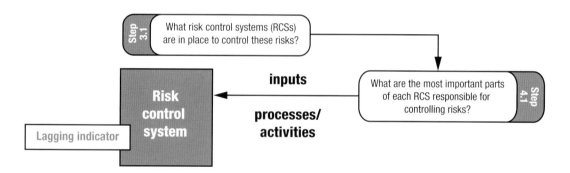

Figure 11 Identify the most important parts of the risk control system

55 It is not necessary to monitor every part of a risk control system. Consider the following factors when determining the aspects to cover:

- Which activities or operations must be undertaken correctly on each and every occasion?
- Which aspects of the system are liable to deterioration over time?
- Which activities are undertaken most frequently?

56 From this, identify the elements of each risk control system that are critical in delivering the outcome. The worked example in **Part 3** illustrates how this process is applied.

Step 4.2: Set leading indicators

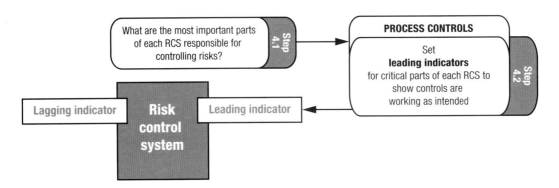

Figure 12 Set leading indicators

57   Once the critical controls to be monitored are determined, **set a leading indicator against each one to show that system is operating as intended**, for example the percentage of safety critical plant inspected to schedule.

> *Leading indicators highlight whether the risk control systems in place to deliver the outcome are operating as designed.*

Step 4.3: Setting tolerances

58   **A tolerance should be set for each leading indicator.** This represents the point at which deviation in performance should be flagged up for attention of senior management. For example, for a leading indicator, 'percentage of overdue safety critical maintenance actions'.

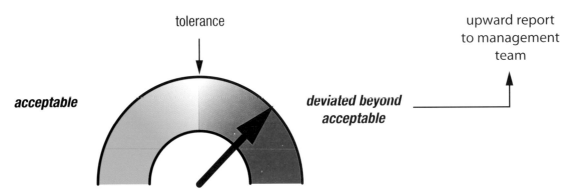

Figure 13 Setting tolerances

59   The tolerance may be set at zero, which means that 100% of actions must be completed on schedule. Alternatively, the company may accept a degree of slippage before it is highlighted to the management team, in which case the tolerance should be set below 100%.

60   **The management team should set the tolerance, not the person responsible for the activity.** This enables management to decide at what point they wish to intervene because performance has deviated beyond an acceptable level.

Step 4.4: Follow up deviations from tolerances

61   Deviations from tolerances must be followed up,
otherwise there is little point in collecting the information.
The main aim of a performance information system is to
indicate where process control management systems have
deteriorated or are not delivering the intended outcome.

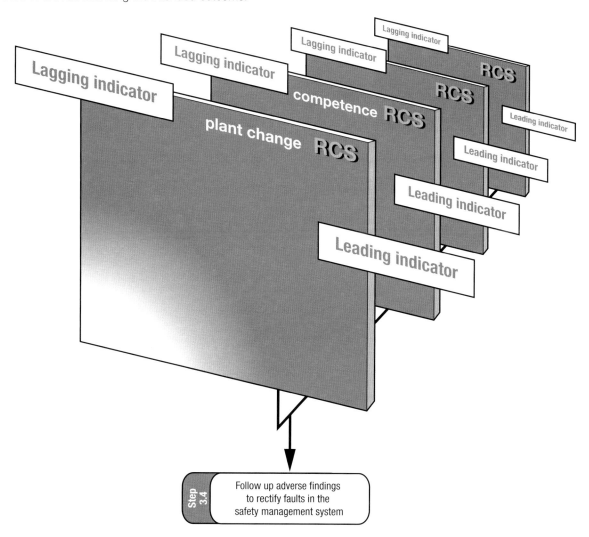

Figure 14 Follow up deviations from tolerances

Step 5: Establish data collection and reporting system

> ■ **Ensure information/unit of measurement for the indicator is available or can be established.**
>
> ■ **Decide on presentation format.**

Collection

62 Once the indicators have been selected and the tolerances set, it is important to ensure that the relevant information is readily available within the organisation. Experience has shown that the information and data required to support a suite of process safety indicators is usually already available and collected for other purposes, eg for quality control or business efficiency. However, it is vital the data is collated to form a complete set of information on process safety risks.

63 Ideally, it is best to co-ordinate the performance data through one person who will be responsible for collecting all the information, compiling reports for the management team and raising the alarm if there are any deviations from set tolerances.

Presentation

64 Keep the presentation of performance data as simple as possible – summarised in a single sheet. It is important to clearly show any deviations from set tolerances or targets and important trends. Graphs, charts or 'dashboards' are probably the best way to show this. Alternatively, various systems such as traffic lights (green – ok, yellow – slight deviation, red – large deviation) or 'smiley/sad faces' (see Table 2) can be used to highlight where you are doing well/badly.

65 The senior management team should regularly receive key performance information. They are the main customers for this information and will need to make decisions on corrective action. There may be a hierarchy of indicators in place, each needing to be collated separately.

66 Present the data to clearly show the link between the lagging indicator (including degree of success against outcome) and the leading indicator(s) relating to the supporting risk control systems. This will clearly highlight the cause-and-effect links between them.

> *Although the presentation of data is important, the data collected is worthless unless it is actually used to improve health and safety.*

Step 6: Review

<table>
<tr><td>The periodic review should include:</td></tr>
</table>

The periodic review should include:

- the performance of the process safety management system;
- the scope of the indicators;
- the tolerances set.

Review performance of the process safety management system

67 Performance against each risk should be routinely reviewed by senior managers to ensure that the whole process safety management system is delivering the intended outcomes, and to provide assurance that critical systems continue to operate as intended.

Variation in performance between leading and lagging indicators

68 If performance is poor against a group of leading indicators but the associated lagging indicator is satisfactory, it is likely that the leading indicators selected are too far removed from the critical control measure that delivers or maintains the desired outcome. For instance, percentage of induction training completed may be measured, whereas more importantly, training and competence in a particular process activity may be more critical to ensuring the safety of that specific activity.

69 If a group of leading indicators are on target and closely linked to the risk control system but the associated lagging indicator shows poor performance, it is likely that risk control system is ineffective in delivering the desired outcome.

Table 2 Leading and lagging indicators for different outcomes

	Outcome 1 (see paragraph 67)	Outcome 2 (see paragraph 67)
Leading indicators		
Lagging indicators		
Potential review issue	Leading indicator too far removed from critical control	Control system ineffective
Potential causes	**Measuring in the wrong place**	**Doing the wrong thing**

Review the scope

70 Indicators should not be decided upon and then forgotten about. Every few years, the scope of the full set of indicators needs to be reviewed to ensure indicators still reflect the main process risks. Indicators may need to be changed because of:

■ introduction of new, high-risk processes;
■ improvement programmes;
■ alteration in plant design;
■ reduction of staff/loss of competence in certain areas.

71 If reviews are not carried out, process safety indicators may become meaningless and the information collected may not give the necessary assurance to senior managers that the major hazard risks are under control.

Review tolerances

72 The importance of following up deviations from tolerances was highlighted in Step 4.4. However, it could be that the tolerance has been set at the wrong point, eg set too leniently/stringently, so the information or data does not adequately reflect reality. In such cases, the tolerance should be reviewed.

> *Tolerances should be reviewed – you don't always get it right first time!*

73 If you would like more information or wish to access HSE's process safety performance website please contact: http://webcommunities.hse.gov.uk/inovem/inovem.ti/chemicalindustries.pspm.

Part 3: Worked example

Steps 2, 3 and 4 of the step-by-step guide

74 This worked example shows how Steps 2-4 of this step-by-step guide have been applied to develop a suite of site-level process safety indicators for a top-tier COMAH bulk chemical storage site.

75 Refer to Steps 2, 3 and 4 in **Part 1** to help work through this example.

Figure 15 Site layout showing the location of the two bulk tank storage facilities and the adjacent dock from where deliveries by ship are made

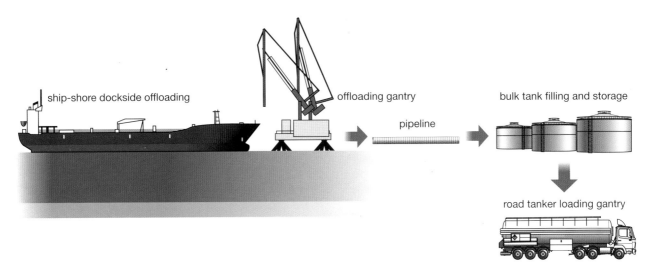

Figure 16 The site and activities

76   The company operates a contract bulk storage business handling liquid chemicals at a top-tier COMAH site comprising of two separate tank farms (formerly owned and operated as two businesses), each containing 80 bulk liquid tanks. Most products are imported by ship and discharged at a jetty on a canal next to an estuary. Shore-side offloading is undertaken by company personnel. Product is transferred to site via fixed pipelines that run across a private field and a small public road. Both sites have road tanker loading gantries.

77   Ship-to-shore transfer is undertaken via articulated gantries with flexible hose connection with screw fitting couplings. Road tanker filling is from fixed overhead gantries with some bottom loading using flexible lines. Clients' contract drivers fill their own vehicles. Both sites are in operation 24 hours a day.

78   All lines between the shore and the installations are cleaned and pigged regularly and bulk tanks often have to be emptied and cleaned to allow for a change of product.

79   Most tanks are mild steel and sit on concrete bases, with earth bunds for groups of tanks and some individual brick bunds. There is on-site production of nitrogen and utilities include a natural gas supply.

80   Highly flammable, toxic and corrosive substances are stored on site, including:

Hexane	Olefin	Dichloromethane
Heptane	Lube oils	Ethylene dibromide
Gasoline	DERV	Trichloromethane
Acetone	Fuel oil	Styrene
Pyridine	Methanol	Caustic soda
	Propanol	Sulphuric acid (98%)

Overview of Steps 2-4

81   The main stages in selecting process safety indicators are:

- Step 2.2: Identify the scope:
  - identify the hazard scenarios that can lead to a major incident; and
  - identify the immediate causes of hazard scenarios.
- Step 3: Identify the risk control systems and describe the 'desired safety outcome' for each – set a lagging indicator:
  - identify the risk control systems in place to prevent or mitigate the effects of the incidents identified;
  - identify the 'desired safety outcomes' of each risk control system; and
  - set a lagging indicator for each risk control system.
- Step 4: Identify critical elements of each risk control system and set a leading indicator:
  - identify the most critical elements of the risk control system and set leading indicators for each element;
  - set a tolerance for each leading indicator; and
  - select the most relevant indicators for the site or activities under consideration.

Step 2.2: Identify the scope

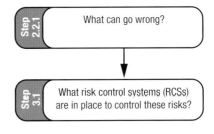

Figure 17 Identify what can go wrong

Step 2.2.1: Identify the hazard scenarios which can lead to a major incident

82 Describing the main incident scenarios helps maintain a focus on the most important activities and controls against which indicators should be set. The scenarios form a useful cross-check later on in Step 4, when the critical elements of risk control systems to be measured are determined.

83 For this site, the main process safety incident scenarios are:

■ Storage tanks:
  - loss of liquid into bunds;
  - loss of liquid outside of the bund;
  - fire and explosion:
  - fire/explosion in a tank;
  - fire in bund;
  - fire outside bund.

■ Docklines and product transfer to bulk storage tanks:
  - loss of liquid from docklines;
  - loss of liquid from fixed pipelines (including couplings, valves, pumps, and flanges);
  - fire at the dockside and from leaks in product transfer pipelines.

■ Road tanker filling:
  - loss of liquid from transfer lines;
  - loss of liquid from a road tanker;
  - fire or explosion in a road tanker;
  - fire in tanker filling area.

84 These events may lead to:

■ a toxic gas cloud or toxic plume;
■ a major fire on the site;
■ a major fire at the dockside;
■ a major fire elsewhere off site, eg next to pipelines; or
■ environmental damage.

Step 2.2.2: Identify the immediate causes of hazard scenarios

85 The immediate cause is the final failure mechanism that gives rise to a loss of containment. This can usually be considered as a factor that challenges the integrity of plant or equipment.

86 Hazard scenarios may be caused by:

■ failure of flexi hose, coupling, pump, valve, fixed pipe work or bulk tank, due to:
  - wear;
  - corrosion;
  - damage;
  - over/under pressurisation; or
  - fire or explosion;
■ overfilling of:
  - bulk tank; or
  - road tanker;
■ accidental release:
  - valves left open, connections not made correctly.

87 Remember to review areas where there are known problems and past incident/near-miss data to help identify the primary causes. This step is important as it is a prerequisite to deciding which risk control systems are important to prevent or control the challenge to integrity.

Primary causes include:

Wear:
■ physical abrasion;
■ vibration/stress.

Corrosion:
■ reaction of mild steel tanks etc from exposure to the atmosphere; or
■ incorrect product transfer/storage or ineffective tank/pipe cleaning, resulting in a chemical reaction from an incompatible product in a tank/pipe or reaction with residues.

Damage:
■ collision/impact, eg by vehicle, plant/equipment;
■ damage during use;
■ ship/tanker driveaway (still attached);
■ work activity, such as welding/grinding; or
■ internal ignition within tanks or external fire affecting structural integrity of the tank.

Over/under pressurisation:
■ incorrect product transfer/storage resulting in lock-in pressure in pipe work, pipe/vent blockage;
■ incorrect nitrogen blanketing of tanks;
■ ineffective tank cleaning leading to an exothermic or endothermic reaction when new product is added.

Fire and explosion:
■ failure to control ignition sources in flammable atmospheres:
  - failure of earth bonding;
  - failure to ensure flow rate is restricted to prevent static accumulation;
  - incorrect equipment selected;
  - failure of nitrogen blanketing of tanks;
  - ignition from damaged or incorrectly selected hazard area electrical equipment;
  - failure to control hot work;
  - failure to stop product movement during electric storms;
  - failure of emergency fire-fighting provision.

Overfilling:
■ incorrect product transfer or incorrect flow rate resulting from:
  - poor communication;
  - instrumentation failure;
  - incorrect product routing; or
  - failure in tank gauging.

Accidental release:
■ leaving valves open;
■ incorrect coupling; or
■ omission of blanking plates etc.

Step 3.1: Identify the associated risk control systems

88 Draw up a risk control matrix as illustrated in Table 3, to help decide which risk control systems are the most important in controlling the challenges to integrity identified within the incident scenarios.

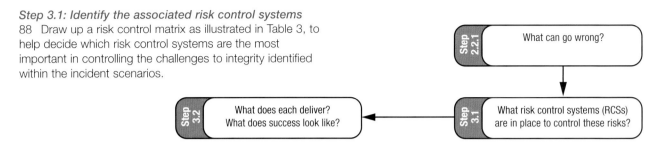

Figure 18 Identify what risk control systems are in place

Table 3 Risk control matrix

	Challenges to plant integrity						
	Wear	Corrosion	Damage	Over/under pressurisation	Fire and explosion	Overfilling	Other accidental release
Inspection and maintenance of:							
Flexi hoses, couplings, pumps, valves, flanges, fixed pipes, bulk tanks	✓	✓	✓		✓		
Instrumentation				✓		✓	
Earth bonding					✓		
Tank vents				✓			
Fire detection and fighting equipment					✓		
Staff competence, covering:							
Selection of compatible tank		✓		✓	✓		
Selection of route and tank with adequate capacity						✓	
Driver error			✓				✓
Correct coupling, opening/closing valves, starting pumps etc				✓			✓
Suitable skills and experience to undertake inspection and maintenance tasks	✓	✓	✓	✓	✓	✓	✓
Emergency arrangements					✓		
Operating procedures, covering:							
Selection of compatible tank		✓		✓			
Selection of route and tank with adequate capacity				✓		✓	
Correct coupling, opening/closing valves, starting pumps etc				✓		✓	✓
Tanker loading						✓	
Ship-to-shore pre- and post-transfer checks				✓		✓	✓
Emergency arrangements					✓		
Instrumentation and alarms				✓		✓	
Plant change							
Selection of correct specification material/equipment	✓	✓			✓		✓
Correct installation/implementation of change	✓	✓			✓		
Communication							
Completion of pre- and post-transfer checks		✓		✓		✓	✓
Instigation of emergency action					✓	✓	✓
Permit to work							
Control of hot work					✓		
Prevention of physical damage/lifting operations			✓				
Safe isolations							✓
Plant design	✓	✓	✓	✓	✓	✓	✓
Emergency arrangements					✓		✓

Wear
89 The main risk control systems for managing the main hazard scenarios are given in Table 4.

Collated list of risk control systems for the installation
90 The following is a summary of the risk control systems relevant to the control and mitigation of the most significant major hazard scenarios associated with the activities on site:

- planned inspection and maintenance;
- staff competence;
- operating procedures;
- instrumentation/alarms;
- plant change;
- plant design;
- communication;
- permit to work;
- earth bonding system; and
- emergency arrangements.

Table 4 Main risk control systems

Hazard scenario	Risk control systems
Wear	Inspection and maintenance Staff competence Plant modification/change, including temporary modifications Plant design
Corrosion	Inspection and maintenance Staff competence Operating procedures Communication Plant change Plant design
Damage	Staff competence (including contractors) Operating procedures Permit to work Workplace transport Inspection and maintenance Plant design
Over/under pressurisation	Staff competence Operating procedures Instrumentation and alarms Communication Inspection and maintenance
Fire and explosion	Permit to work Plant inspection and maintenance – especially electrical equipment Staff competence Operating procedures Plant change Plant design Earth bonding system
Overfilling	Staff competence Operating procedures Instrumentation/alarms Communication
Accidental release	Staff competence Operating procedures Permit to work Communication
Emergency arrangements	For any of the scenarios listed above, it is important to mitigate the consequences of an incident or loss of containment. This risk control system is therefore included in the overall list of systems in place at this establishment

Step 3: Identify the outcome and set a lagging indicator

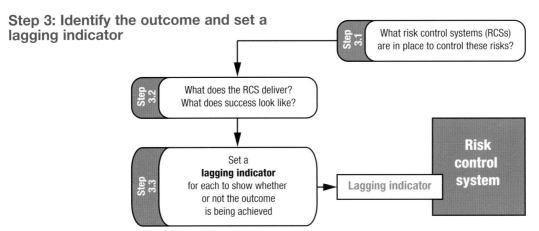

Figure 19 Identify the outcome and set a lagging indicator

91 It is vital to discuss and agree the reason why each risk control system is in place and what it achieves in terms of the scenarios identified. Without this agreement, it will be impossible to measure success in delivering this outcome.

92 It is best to phrase 'success' in terms of a positive outcome – supportive of the safety and business priorities. The indicator can then be set as a positive or negative metric to flag up when this is achieved or when not. As success should be the normal outcome, choosing a negative metric will guard against being swamped by data (reporting by exception).

93 The following questions may be helpful:

- Why do we have this risk control system in place?
- What does it deliver in terms of safety?
- What would be the consequence if we didn't have this system in place?

94 The indicator set should be directly linked to the agreed risk control system outcome and should be able to measure the success/failure at meeting the outcome.

Step 4: Identify the critical elements of each risk control system and set leading indicators

95 There are too many elements to a risk control system for each to be measured. It is not necessary to monitor every part of a risk control system. Consider the following factors when deciding which aspects to include:

- Which activities or operations must be undertaken correctly on each and every occasion?
- Which aspects of the system are liable to deteriorate over time?
- Which activities are undertaken most frequently?

96 From this, the critical elements of each risk control system important to delivering the outcome can be identified.

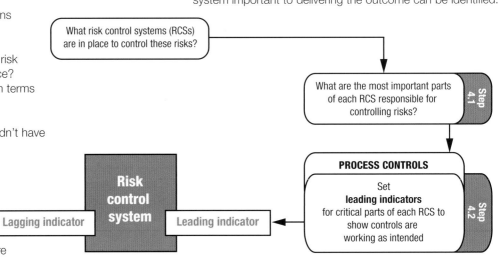

Figure 20 Identify critical elements and set leading indicators

Examples of indicators for each risk control system

97 The following section illustrates how Steps 3 and 4 are used to identify indicators for each important risk control system in the process safety management system in place at the installation. Initially, a number of outcomes and subsequent candidate lagging and leading indicators are generated. These are then prioritised to select just one lagging indicator and a maximum of two leading indicators for each risk control system. The final selection for all the risk control systems is given in Table 3.

Risk control systems

RCS: Inspection and maintenance

Desired safety outcomes

- No unexpected loss of containment due to failure of flexi hoses, couplings, pumps, valves, flanges, fixed pipes, bulk tanks or instrumentation.
- No unexpected loss of containment due to blockages in tank vents.
- No fires or explosions due to static electric ignition.
- No fires or explosions caused by a source of ignition from faulty or damaged hazardous area electrical equipment.
- Fire detection and fire-fighting equipment is available and in good condition.

Potential lagging indicators

- Number of unexpected loss-of-containment incidents due to failure of flexi hoses, couplings, pumps, valves, flanges, fixed pipes, bulk tanks or instrumentation.
- Number of loss-of-containments due to blockages in tank vents.
- Number of fires or explosions that result from a static electric ignition.
- Number of fires or explosions caused by a source of ignition from faulty or damaged hazardous area electrical equipment.
- Number of incidents of fire/explosion where fire detection or fire-fighting equipment failed to function as designed.

Critical elements

- The specification of scope and frequency of the inspection and maintenance system. This should be based on how safety critical the item is, and on the degree of challenge presented to the system integrity, or to comply with the manufacturer's or supplier's instructions.
- Safety critical plant and equipment (ie flexi hoses, couplings, pumps valves, flanges, fixed pipes, bulk tanks) are inspected for wear and damage or malfunction within the specified period.
- Faults are fixed within specified timescales and repairs and improvements meet plant design standards.
- A log of findings kept – enabling trending.

Potential leading indicators

- Percentage of safety critical plant/equipment that performs within specification when inspected.
- Percentage of safety critical plant and equipment inspections completed to schedule.
- Percentage of maintenance actions identified that are completed to the specified timescale.
- Percentage of fault trending carried out to schedule.

Final selection of indicators

It is often difficult to choose only a limited number of indicators from the range of potential candidates generated within Steps 3.3 (lagging indicators) and Steps 4.2 (leading indicators). To prioritise, consider:

- Is the outcome measurable, ie can a successful or adverse outcome easily be detected? Ask 'would you know when this had happened?'
- Is a critical control or activity measurable, ie can the correct operation of a critical control easily be detected?
- How often can each be measured?
- For lagging indicators: how much information is it likely to generate? Aim for reporting by exception.
- For leading indicators: how susceptible are critical elements of the system to rapid deterioration?
- Will the indicator highlight abnormal conditions before a serious event occurs?
- Recheck that the indicators:
  - support the outcomes set; and
  - that leading indicators link to the lagging indicator.
- What is the overall importance, in terms of safety and business priorities, of the information provided by the indicator?
- Can the information be readily collected, ie is it already recorded somewhere in the organisation, eg noted in quality logs/records or process control records?

Note: What constitutes a 'safety critical' item should have been identified while considering major accident scenarios.

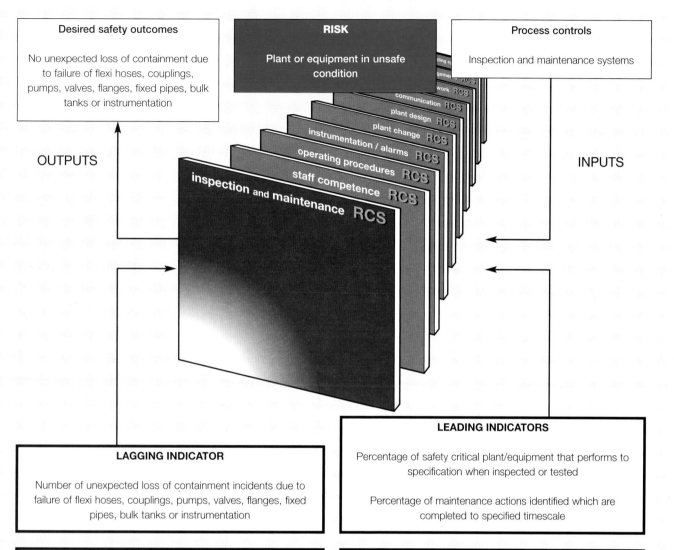

<table>
<tr><td>

Desired safety outcomes

No unexpected loss of containment due to failure of flexi hoses, couplings, pumps, valves, flanges, fixed pipes, bulk tanks or instrumentation

</td><td>

RISK

Plant or equipment in unsafe condition

</td><td>

Process controls

Inspection and maintenance systems

</td></tr>
</table>

OUTPUTS

INPUTS

management RCS
work RCS
communication RCS
plant design RCS
plant change RCS
instrumentation / alarms RCS
operating procedures RCS
staff competence RCS
inspection and maintenance RCS

LAGGING INDICATOR

Number of unexpected loss of containment incidents due to failure of flexi hoses, couplings, pumps, valves, flanges, fixed pipes, bulk tanks or instrumentation

LEADING INDICATORS

Percentage of safety critical plant/equipment that performs to specification when inspected or tested

Percentage of maintenance actions identified which are completed to specified timescale

---

Justification

This indicator covers the widest range of equipment where most problems are likely to occur. This indicator could be narrowed down further to focus on specific items of plant considered to present the highest risk, eg flexible hoses

Justification

Performance of safety critical equipment
This indicator shows the reliability of plant and equipment but also provides the means to explore why equipment may not have performed as intended. Also, to arrive at this information, the scheduled inspection actions will need to have been completed

Completion of maintenance actions
It is important to get a complete picture of any backlog of faults associated with safety critical plant. Again, the inspection and maintenance schedule will have to have been undertaken to obtain this information

---

Lagging indicators discounted
- Tank vent blockages: these events can be captured in the indicator covering the failure of bulk tanks.
- Static ignition: it can be difficult to be certain whether a fire/explosion occurred as a result of a static electric ignition. Such events should be quite rare and if they do occur they can be picked up as part of incident investigation.
- Number of fires or explosions caused by a source of ignition from faulty or damaged hazardous area electrical equipment: these should be very rare events and so of little benefit due to the low frequency.
- Fire detection and fire-fighting equipment: such events are likely to be rare. Identification of failings in detection and fire-fighting equipment is better covered under RCS: Emergency arrangements.

Leading indicators discounted
- Progress with inspection schedule: this is a frequently used indicator. However, the indicator on performance of safety critical equipment is much closer to the desired outcome.
- Fault trending: although fault trending is important, measuring the percentage of the trending actions completed may not provide good assurance that problems with reliability are being rectified.

Figure 21 Inspection and maintenance indicators

RCS: Staff competence

Outcomes

- Operators and contractors have the required knowledge and skills to enable effective product transfer from ship, to bulk tank, to road tanker.
- Operators and contractors have the required knowledge and skills to adequately clean bulk tanks/pipelines before/after a product transfer.
- Operators and contractors have the required knowledge and skills to take emergency action following a product transfer that results in a fire/explosion.

Potential lagging indicators

- Number of times product transfer does not proceed as planned due to errors made by staff without the necessary understanding, knowledge or experience to take correct actions.
- Number of times a bulk tank is over/under pressurised due to inadequate cleaning by staff without the necessary understanding, knowledge or experience.
- Number of times ineffective action is taken following a product transfer resulting in fire/explosion, due to lack of understanding, knowledge or experience to take correct emergency action.

Critical elements

Information and training covering:

- hazardous properties of products;
- ship-to-shore communication systems;
- pre-transfer checks;
- product transfer controls and monitoring;
- post-transfer checks;
- emergency actions.

Job-specific knowledge and relevant experience of:

- substances;
- work processes;
- hazards; and
- emergency actions.

Potential leading indicators

- Percentage of staff involved in product transfers who have the required level of competence necessary for the successful transfer and storage of products.

Note: The company will determine the type of training and experience necessary to achieve competence.

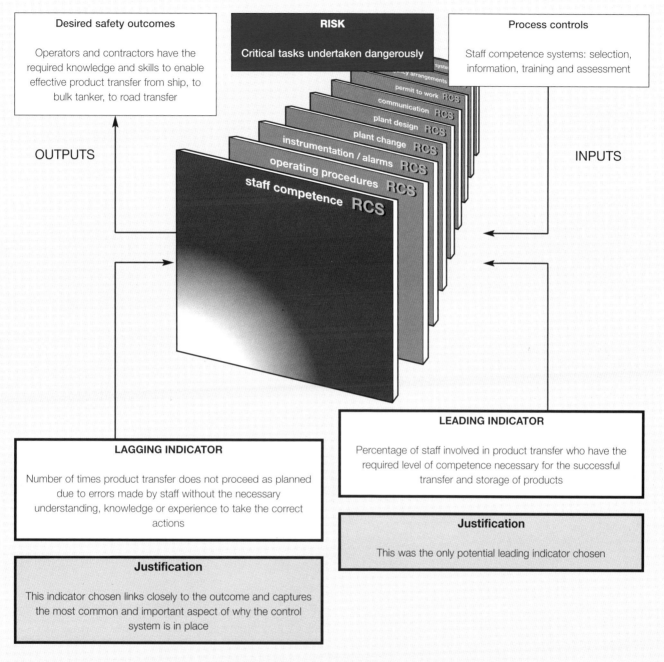

Desired safety outcomes	RISK	Process controls
Operators and contractors have the required knowledge and skills to enable effective product transfer from ship, to bulk tanker, to road transfer	Critical tasks undertaken dangerously	Staff competence systems: selection, information, training and assessment

OUTPUTS

INPUTS

emergency arrangements system
permit to work RCS
communication RCS
plant design RCS
plant change RCS
instrumentation / alarms RCS
operating procedures RCS
staff competence RCS

LAGGING INDICATOR

Number of times product transfer does not proceed as planned due to errors made by staff without the necessary understanding, knowledge or experience to take the correct actions

LEADING INDICATOR

Percentage of staff involved in product transfer who have the required level of competence necessary for the successful transfer and storage of products

Justification

This indicator chosen links closely to the outcome and captures the most common and important aspect of why the control system is in place

Justification

This was the only potential leading indicator chosen

Lagging indicators discounted

- Tank over/under pressurisation: ensuring competence for tank cleaning is unlikely to be a complex or demanding issue that may frequently give rise to incidents caused by lack of competence. It is therefore more appropriate to measure other aspects of competence.
- Emergency action: this is better covered under RCS: Emergency Arrangements.

Figure 22 Staff competence indicators

RCS: Operating procedures

Desired safety outcomes

■ Correct tank selection and operation of equipment during product transfer from ship, to bulk tank, to road tanker.

■ Correct cleaning, isolation and equipment shutdown after product transfer.

Potential lagging indicators

■ Number of times product transfer does not occur as planned due to incorrect/unclear operational procedures.

■ Number of times a bulk tank is over/under pressurised due to inadequate cleaning by staff working with unclear/incorrect operational procedures.

■ Number of times ineffective action is taken following a product transfer resulting in fire/explosion due to incorrect/unclear operational procedures.

Critical elements

■ Procedures contain correct scope (key actions and tasks including emergency action) and/or sufficient detail.

■ Procedures are clearly written/easily understood.

■ Procedures are kept up to date.

Potential leading indicators

■ Percentage of safety critical tasks for which a written operational procedure covers the correct scope (key actions and tasks including emergency action) and/or sufficient detail.

■ Percentage of procedures that are clearly written and easy to understand.

■ Percentage of procedures that are reviewed and revised within the designated period.

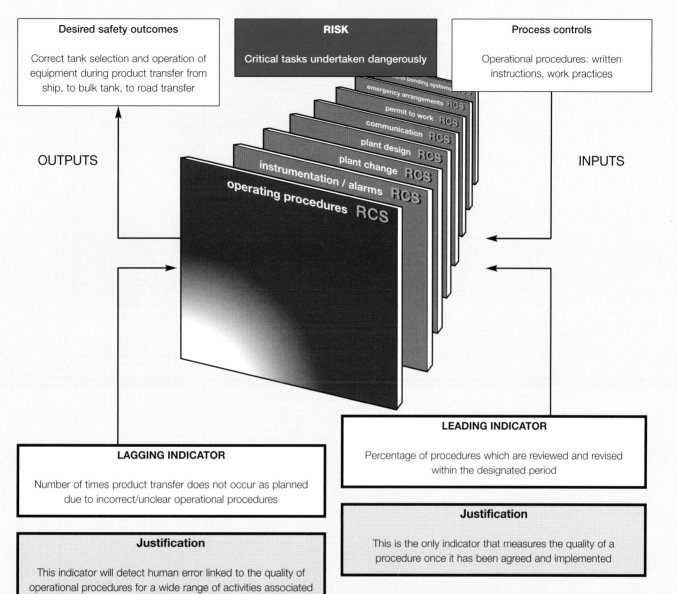

Desired safety outcomes

Correct tank selection and operation of equipment during product transfer from ship, to bulk tank, to road transfer

RISK

Critical tasks undertaken dangerously

Process controls

Operational procedures: written instructions, work practices

OUTPUTS   INPUTS

earth bonding systems RCS
emergency arrangements RCS
permit to work RCS
communication RCS
plant design RCS
plant change RCS
instrumentation / alarms RCS
operating procedures RCS

LEADING INDICATOR

Percentage of procedures which are reviewed and revised within the designated period

LAGGING INDICATOR

Number of times product transfer does not occur as planned due to incorrect/unclear operational procedures

Justification

This is the only indicator that measures the quality of a procedure once it has been agreed and implemented

Justification

This indicator will detect human error linked to the quality of operational procedures for a wide range of activities associated with the outcome

Leading indicators discounted
- Scope and clarity of procedures: this should be ensured by a one-off check carried out before the procedure is first introduced and cannot be usefully monitored on an ongoing basis.

Lagging indicators discounted
- Tank over/under pressurisation: it is better to focus on a wider set of activities reliant on good operating procedures as covered by the indicator chosen, because this will provide a more comprehensive picture of the suitability of written procedures.
- Emergency action: this is better covered under RCS: Emergency Arrangements.

Figure 23 Operating procedure indicators

RCS: Instrumentation and alarms

Desired safety outcomes
- Safety critical instrumentation and alarms correctly indicate when process conditions exceed safe operating limits.

Potential lagging indicators
- Number of safety critical instruments/alarms that fail to operate as designed, either in use or during testing.
- Number of times a bulk tank or a road tanker is overfilled due to failure in the level indicator or alarms.
- Number of times a bulk tank or a road tanker is over/under pressurised due to failure in a level indicator or alarms.
- Number of times product is transferred at the wrong flow rate or pressure due to failure in a flow meter/pressure gauge or alarms.

Critical elements
- Instruments correctly indicate process conditions.
- Alarms activate at desired set points.
- Instruments and alarms are tested and calibrated to design standard.
- Repairs to faulty instruments and alarms are carried out within specified time period.

Potential leading indicators
- Percentage of safety critical instruments and alarms that correctly indicate the process conditions.
- Percentage of safety critical instruments and alarms that activate at the desired set point.
- Percentage of functional tests of safety critical instruments and alarms completed to schedule.
- Percentage of maintenance actions to rectify faults to safety critical instruments and alarms completed to schedule.

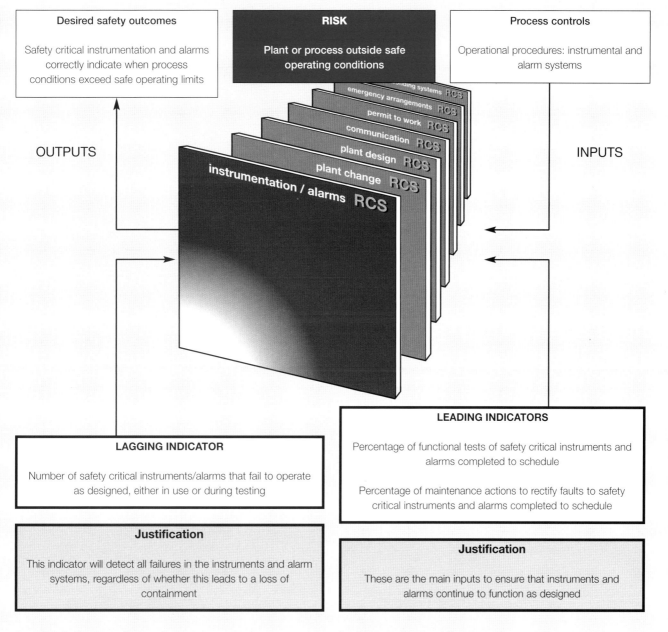

Desired safety outcomes

Safety critical instrumentation and alarms correctly indicate when process conditions exceed safe operating limits

RISK

Plant or process outside safe operating conditions

Process controls

Operational procedures: instrumental and alarm systems

OUTPUTS

INPUTS

...nding systems RCS
emergency arrangements RCS
permit to work RCS
communication RCS
plant design RCS
plant change RCS
instrumentation / alarms RCS

LAGGING INDICATOR

Number of safety critical instruments/alarms that fail to operate as designed, either in use or during testing

LEADING INDICATORS

Percentage of functional tests of safety critical instruments and alarms completed to schedule

Percentage of maintenance actions to rectify faults to safety critical instruments and alarms completed to schedule

Justification

This indicator will detect all failures in the instruments and alarm systems, regardless of whether this leads to a loss of containment

Justification

These are the main inputs to ensure that instruments and alarms continue to function as designed

Lagging indicators discounted
- Number of times a bulk tank or a road tanker is overfilled due to failure in a level indicator or alarm.
- Number of times a bulk tank or a road tanker is over/under pressurised due to failure in a level indicator or alarm.
- Number of times product is transferred at the wrong flow rate or pressure due to failure in a flow meter, pressure gauge or alarm.

All of these indicators are a subset of the preferred indicator selected.

Leading indicators discounted
- Percentage of safety critical instruments and alarms that correctly indicate the process conditions.
- Percentage of safety critical instruments and alarms that activate at the desired set point.

These two indicators will be covered within the functional testing and maintenance system.

Note: Instrumentation and alarm system functioning can be considered as an important part of a wider inspection and maintenance system and the indicators set in this section could be readily incorporated into the broader inspection/maintenance scheme and measured as part of that system.

Figure 24 Instrumentation and alarm indicators

RCS: Plant change

Desired safety outcomes
- Following a change of specification of flexi hoses, couplings, pumps, fixed pipes, bulk tanks, they continue to operate in an optimised state.

Potential lagging indicators
- Number of incidents involving loss of containment of hazardous material or fire/explosion due to failure of flexi hoses, couplings, valves, pumps, fixed pipes, bulk tanks, where plant change was found to be a contributory factor.
- Number of times equipment or plant is below the desired standard due to deficiencies in plant change.

Critical elements
- Scope and definition are properly set out (temporary/permanent changes).
- Risk assessments are undertaken before plant change.
- Changes/outcomes are documented.
- Changes are authorised before being implemented.
- Post-change checks are carried out (plant found to be performing as designed).

Potential leading indicators
- The scope and definition of the plant change system is properly specified.
- Percentage of plant change actions undertaken where an adequate risk assessment was carried out before change.
- Percentage of plant change actions undertaken where changes/outcomes were documented.
- Percentage of plant change actions undertaken where authorisation was given before implementation.
- Percentage of plant change actions undertaken where post-change checks were carried out.

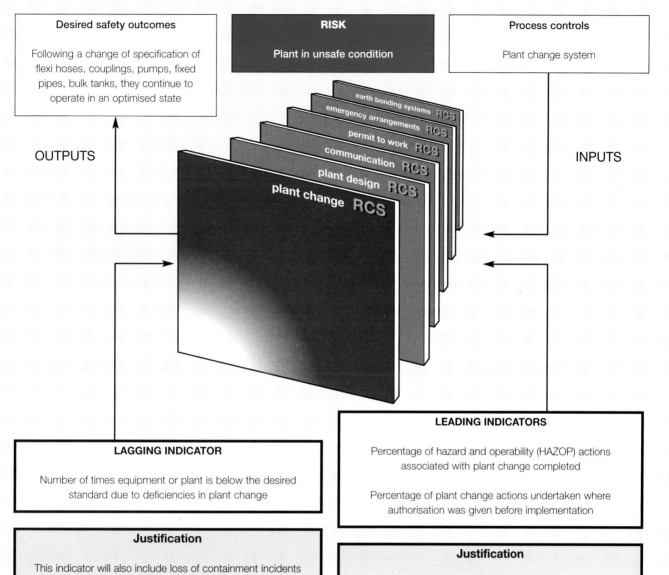

OUTPUTS

INPUTS

Desired safety outcomes	RISK	Process controls
Following a change of specification of flexi hoses, couplings, pumps, fixed pipes, bulk tanks, they continue to operate in an optimised state	Plant in unsafe condition	Plant change system

earth bonding systems RCS
emergency arrangements RCS
permit to work RCS
communication RCS
plant design RCS
plant change RCS

LAGGING INDICATOR

Number of times equipment or plant is below the desired standard due to deficiencies in plant change

Justification

This indicator will also include loss of containment incidents where these are due to deficient plant or equipment following a plant change

Lagging indicators discounted
- Number of incidents involving loss of containment of hazardous material or fire/explosion due to failure of flexi hoses, couplings, valves, pumps, fixed pipes, bulk tanks where deficiency in plant change was found to be a contributory factor.

The first indicator will capture these sorts of events automatically if the cause is attributed to a fault following a plant change.

LEADING INDICATORS

Percentage of hazard and operability (HAZOP) actions associated with plant change completed

Percentage of plant change actions undertaken where authorisation was given before implementation

Justification

Completion of risk assessments
This is a critical aspect of plant change upon which the outcome is dependent. It is likely to be easy to measure and capture the relevant information

Retrospective authorisations
This indicator will show where potentially dangerous circumstances may be created due to a need to implement changes quickly

Leading indicators discounted
- Documentation of changes.
- Post-change checks.

Both of these indicators are important and it is relatively easy to collect information against them. However, they were not selected simply to keep the overall number of indicators to a reasonable level.

Figure 25 Plant change indicators

RCS: Plant design

Desired safety outcome
- Plant operation optimised with equipment running efficiently and reliably with no unexpected breakdown due to deficiencies in the plant design and specification.

Potential lagging indicator
- Number of plant breakdowns or incidents involving loss of containment of hazardous material or failure of safety critical plant/equipment where deficiency in plant design was found to be a contributory factor.

Critical elements
When selecting suitable equipment, consider:

- standards and codes;
- compatibility of materials with products;
- anticipated duty and degradation methods;
- pressure systems;
- life expectancy;
- electrical integrity and equipment bonding; and
- ease of inspection and maintenance.

Potential leading indicators
- Percentage of equipment and plant associated with product transfer that meets current standards and codes.
- On commissioning: percentage of safety critical items of plant or equipment which comply with specified design standards.
- On a periodic basis: percentage of safety critical items of plant or equipment which comply with current design standards or codes.

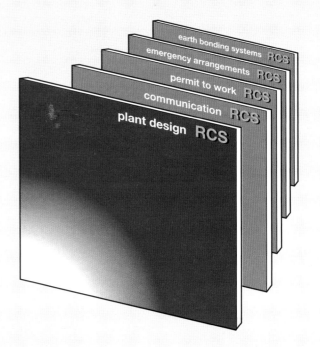

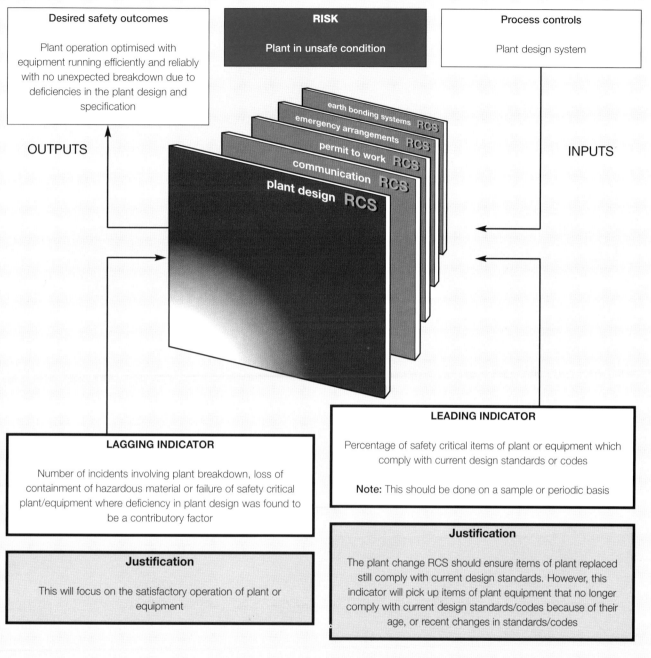

Desired safety outcomes

Plant operation optimised with equipment running efficiently and reliably with no unexpected breakdown due to deficiencies in the plant design and specification

RISK

Plant in unsafe condition

Process controls

Plant design system

OUTPUTS

INPUTS

earth bonding systems **RCS**
emergency arrangements **RCS**
permit to work **RCS**
communication **RCS**
plant design **RCS**

LEADING INDICATOR

Percentage of safety critical items of plant or equipment which comply with current design standards or codes

Note: This should be done on a sample or periodic basis

LAGGING INDICATOR

Number of incidents involving plant breakdown, loss of containment of hazardous material or failure of safety critical plant/equipment where deficiency in plant design was found to be a contributory factor

Justification

This will focus on the satisfactory operation of plant or equipment

Justification

The plant change RCS should ensure items of plant replaced still comply with current design standards. However, this indicator will pick up items of plant equipment that no longer comply with current design standards/codes because of their age, or recent changes in standards/codes

Leading indicators discounted

- On commissioning: the percentage of safety critical items of plant or equipment which comply with specified design standards.
- On a periodic basis: percentage of critical items of plant or equipment which comply with current design standards or codes.

These are one-off checks that do not benefit from being measured throughout the year.

Figure 26 Plant design indicators

RCS: Communication

Desired safety outcomes
- Effective management of product transfer* and storage and effective warning of problems in time to take remedial action.
- Effective remedial action is taken in the event of overfill, fire/explosion or accidental release.

* Product transfer includes all aspects and actions associated with the successful transfer of hazardous material from ship to shore into bulk storage or between bulk tanks and the filling or discharge of road tankers.

Potential lagging indicators
- Number of times product transfer does not proceed as planned due to breakdown in communication systems. This outcome could be subdivided into two further indicators, ie:
- number of times overfilling occurs due to a breakdown in communication systems;
- number of times accidental releases occur due to breakdown in communication systems.
- Percentage of mitigating systems which failed to operate following an overfill, fire/explosion or accidental release due to failure to adequately communicate information relating to the emergency.

Critical elements
Critical communications undertaken:

- Confirmation of pre-transfer checks –·type, properties, quantity of material to be transferred.
- Confirmation of route integrity, connections made, valves open.
- Authorisation to start transfer.
- Confirmation of start/rate of transfer.
- Confirmation of containment integrity checks carried out during transfers.
- Post-transfer – confirmation of pumps stopped, valves closed.

Potential leading indicators
- Percentage of product transfers where confirmation of the completion of pre-transfer checks was adequately communicated.
- Percentage of product transfers where confirmation of route integrity, connections made, valves open etc was adequately communicated.
- Percentage of product transfers where authorisation to start transfer was successfully completed before transfer commenced.
- Percentage of product transfers where confirmation of start and rate of transfer were successfully completed before transfer commenced.
- Percentage of product transfers where confirmation of start and rate of transfer were successfully completed before transfer commenced.
- Percentage of containment integrity checks carried out during transfers.
- Percentage of post-transfer checks undertaken to confirm that pumps have stopped and valves are isolated or closed.

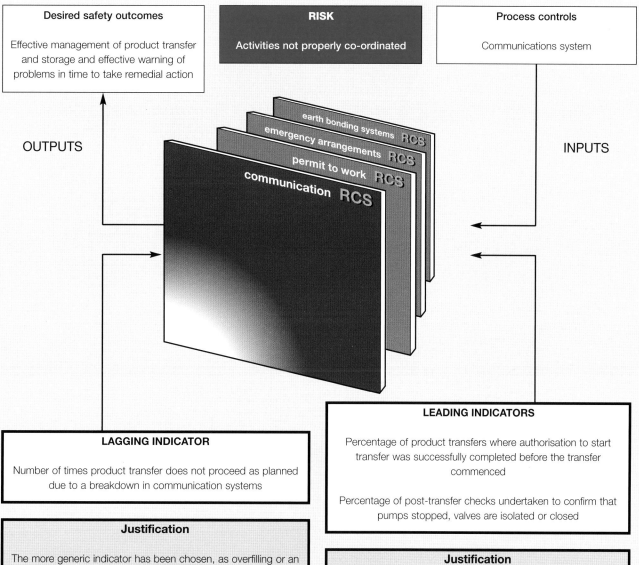

Desired safety outcomes	RISK	Process controls
Effective management of product transfer and storage and effective warning of problems in time to take remedial action	Activities not properly co-ordinated	Communications system

OUTPUTS

INPUTS

earth bonding systems RCS
emergency arrangements RCS
permit to work RCS
communication RCS

LAGGING INDICATOR

Number of times product transfer does not proceed as planned due to a breakdown in communication systems

Justification

The more generic indicator has been chosen, as overfilling or an accidental release could not be considered as 'a planned, successful product transfer'. Therefore, both these events would be captured within the first indicator. Also this broader category offers the opportunity to capture a wider series of events, some of which may not have been fully considered when formulating the indicators

LEADING INDICATORS

Percentage of product transfers where authorisation to start transfer was successfully completed before the transfer commenced

Percentage of post-transfer checks undertaken to confirm that pumps stopped, valves are isolated or closed

Justification

This first indicator automatically captures all the other checks that should be completed before authorisation is issued. The second ensures that the plant is secured in a safe condition after the activity

Lagging indicators discounted
■ Failure of mitigation: incidents with this type of cause are likely to be very rare. This is better covered under RCS: Emergency arrangements.

Leading indicators discounted
■ Percentage of product transfers where confirmation of completion of pre-transfer checks was adequately communicated.
■ Percentage of product transfers where confirmation of route integrity, connections made, valves open etc was adequately communicated.
■ Percentage of product transfers where confirmation of start and rate of transfer were successfully completed before product transfer commenced.
■ Percentage of product transfers where the confirmation of start and rate of transfer were successfully completed before product transfer commenced.

Again, ensure that the final authorisation is issued automatically and includes the checks listed above.

Figure 27 Communication indicators

RCS: Permit to work

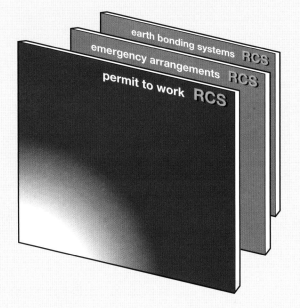

Desired safety outcome
- High-risk maintenance activities are undertaken in a way that will not cause damage/injury.

Potential lagging indicator
- Number of incidents where plant/equipment could be damaged due to failure to control high-risk maintenance activity.

Critical elements
- Scope of activities covered by the permit-to-work system is clearly identified.
- Permits specify the hazards, risks and control measures, including isolations.
- Permits are only issued following suitable authorisation procedures.
- Permit/task is time limited.
- Work is conducted as per permit conditions, including demonstration of satisfactory completion of work.

Potential leading indicators
- The scope and definition of the permit-to-work system has been properly specified.
- Percentage of permits to work issued where the hazards, risks and control measures were adequately specified.
- Percentage of permits issued where the time period for completing the task is specified.
- Percentage of work conducted in accordance with permit conditions and where completion of work has been demonstrated.

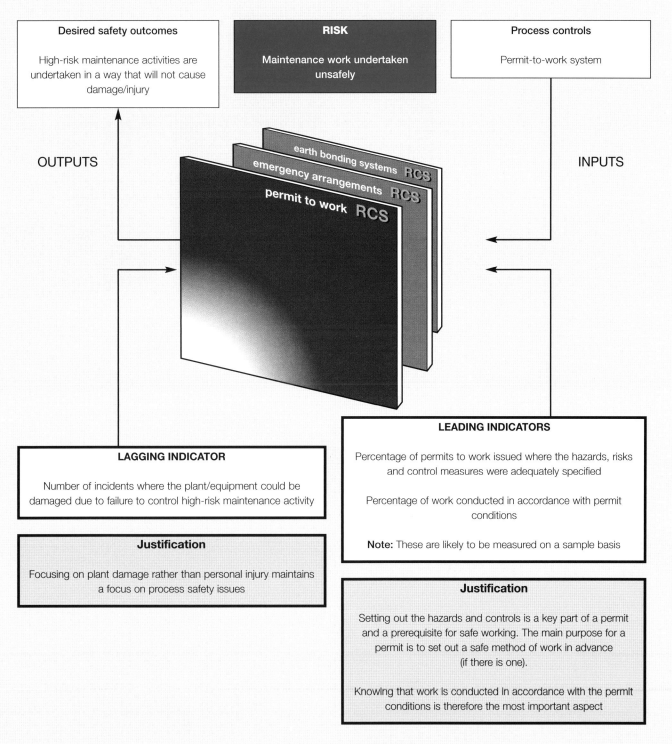

Desired safety outcomes

High-risk maintenance activities are undertaken in a way that will not cause damage/injury

RISK

Maintenance work undertaken unsafely

Process controls

Permit-to-work system

OUTPUTS

INPUTS

earth bonding systems RCS
emergency arrangements RCS
permit to work RCS

LAGGING INDICATOR

Number of incidents where the plant/equipment could be damaged due to failure to control high-risk maintenance activity

Justification

Focusing on plant damage rather than personal injury maintains a focus on process safety issues

LEADING INDICATORS

Percentage of permits to work issued where the hazards, risks and control measures were adequately specified

Percentage of work conducted in accordance with permit conditions

Note: These are likely to be measured on a sample basis

Justification

Setting out the hazards and controls is a key part of a permit and a prerequisite for safe working. The main purpose for a permit is to set out a safe method of work in advance (if there is one).

Knowing that work is conducted in accordance with the permit conditions is therefore the most important aspect

Leading indicators discounted
- The scope and definition of the permit-to-work system has been properly specified: this is a one-off activity and unlikely to deteriorate over time.
- Time period specified: although this is important, it not considered as critical as authorisation before work starts.

Figure 28 Permit-to-work indicators

RCS: Emergency arrangements

Desired safety outcome
■ The impact of a major incident during product transfer or storage is minimised as far as possible.

Potential lagging indicator
■ Number of elements of the emergency procedure that fail to function to the designed performance standard.

System critical elements
■ Emergency plan covers all relevant operations.
■ Testing of emergency plan.
■ Raising alarm.
■ Shutdown/isolation procedures.
■ Fire fighting – starting fire pumps.
■ Communication with ship/installation control rooms, and immediate site neighbours.
■ Evacuation – ship/dock/site.
■ Communication with the dock operating company.
■ Communication with emergency services.

Potential leading indicators
■ Percentage of shutdown/isolation systems that functioned to the desired performance standard when tested.
■ Percentage of times the fire-fighting pumps started automatically and pressurised the fire main when the alarm was tested.
■ Percentage of staff/contractors who take the correct action in the event of an emergency.
■ Percentage of staff/contractors trained in emergency arrangements.
■ Percentage of emergency exercises completed to schedule.

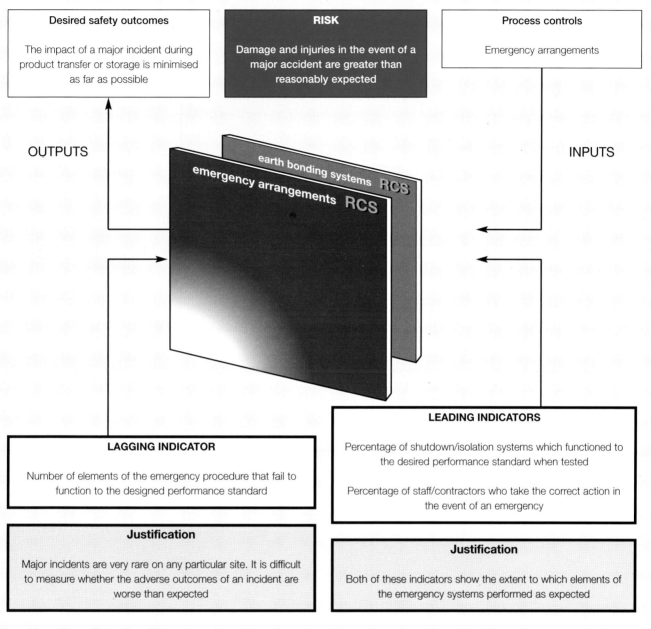

Desired safety outcomes The impact of a major incident during product transfer or storage is minimised as far as possible	**RISK** Damage and injuries in the event of a major accident are greater than reasonably expected	**Process controls** Emergency arrangements

OUTPUTS

INPUTS

earth bonding systems RCS

emergency arrangements RCS

LAGGING INDICATOR

Number of elements of the emergency procedure that fail to function to the designed performance standard

LEADING INDICATORS

Percentage of shutdown/isolation systems which functioned to the desired performance standard when tested

Percentage of staff/contractors who take the correct action in the event of an emergency

Justification

Major incidents are very rare on any particular site. It is difficult to measure whether the adverse outcomes of an incident are worse than expected

Justification

Both of these indicators show the extent to which elements of the emergency systems performed as expected

Leading indicators discounted
- Percentage of times the fire-fighting pumps started automatically and pressurised the fire main when the alarm was tested: this is a fairly narrow set of circumstances which would already be captured by the first indicator.
- Percentage of staff/contractors trained in emergency arrangements: this indicator doesn't provide information on the function of the system and so is further away from the outcome.
- Percentage of emergency exercises completed to schedule: this indicator doesn't provide information on the function of the system and so is further away from the outcome.

Figure 29 Emergency arrangement indicators

RCS: Earth bonding

Desired safety outcome
- Static electric charge, caused by product movement/flow, is dissipated without giving rise to ignition.

Potential lagging indicator
- Number of incidents involving fire and explosion caused by static ignition.

Critical elements
- All important elements are correctly bonded together and connected to the earth.
- Impedance is sufficiently low to allow effective discharge of current.
- Continuity of earth bonding is routinely checked.

Potential leading indicators
- Percentage of at-risk plant where the earth bonding is in place.
- Percentage of safety critical plant where impedance of the earth bonding system is to specification.

Indicators selected
- None of these indicators were chosen because the integrity of earth bonding should be checked within the inspection and maintenance systems and can be measured as part of that wider scheme.

Table 5 Final suite of process safety performance indicators for the whole installation

Control	Lagging indicator	Leading indicator
Inspection/ maintenance	Number of unexpected loss-of-containment incidents due to failure of flexi hoses, couplings, pumps, valves, flanges, fixed pipes, bulk tanks or instrumentation.	Percentage of safety critical plant/equipment that performs to specification when inspected or tested. Percentage of maintenance actions identified which are completed to specified timescale.
Staff competence	Number of times product transfer does not proceed as planned due to errors made by staff without the necessary understanding, knowledge or experience to take correct actions.	Percentage of staff involved in product transfer who have the required level of competence necessary for the successful transfer and storage of products. **Note:** the company will determine the type of training and experience necessary to achieve competence.
Operational procedures	Number of times product transfer does not occur as planned due to incorrect/unclear operational procedures.	Percentage of procedures which are reviewed/revised within the designated period.
Instrumentation and alarms	Number of safety critical instrumentation/alarms that fail to operate as designed either in use or during testing.	Percentage of functional tests of safety critical instruments and alarms completed to schedule. Percentage of maintenance actions to rectify faults to safety critical instruments and alarms completed to schedule.
Plant change	Number of times equipment or plant is below the desired standard due to deficiencies in plant change.	Percentage of plant change actions undertaken where an adequate risk assessment was carried out before change. Percentage of plant change actions undertaken where authorisation was given before implementation.
Communication	Number of times product transfer does not proceed as planned due to a breakdown in communication systems.	Percentage of product transfers where authorisation to start transfer was successfully completed before the transfer commenced. Percentage of post-transfer checks undertaken to confirm that pumps have stopped, and valves are isolated or closed.
Permit to work	Number of incidents where plant/equipment could be damaged due to failure to control high-risk maintenance activity.	Percentage of permits to work issued where the hazards, risks and control measures were adequately specified. Percentage of work conducted in accordance with permit conditions. **Note:** These are likely to be measured on a sample basis.
Plant design	Number of incidents involving breakdown, loss of containment of hazardous material or failure of safety critical plant/equipment, where deficiency in plant design was found to be a contributory factor.	Percentage of safety critical items of plant or equipment which comply with current design standards or codes. **Note:** This should be done on a sample or periodic basis.
Emergency arrangements	Number of elements of the emergency procedure that fail to function to the designed performance standard.	Percentage of shutdown/isolation systems which functioned to the desired performance standard when tested. Percentage of staff/contractors who take the correct action in the event of an emergency.

References and further information

References

1   *Major incident investigation report, BP Grangemouth Scotland, 29 May – 10 June 2000 COMAH* Competent Authority Report August 2003
www.hse.gov.uk/comah/bparrange/index.htm

2   *Responsible Care. An Introduction* RC107 Chemical Industries Association London 1999

3   *Control of Major Accident Hazards Regulations 1999 SI 1999/743 The Stationery Office 1999 ISBN 0 11 082192 0 (COMAH), as amended by the Control of Major Accident Hazards (Amendment) Regulations 2005* SI 2005/1088 The Stationery Office 2005 ISBN 0 11 072766 5, which implements the Seveso II Directive (96/82/EC) in Great Britain

4   *Successful health and safety management* HSG65 (Second edition) HSE Books 1997 ISBN 0 7176 1276 7

5   *Responsible Care Management Systems Guidance* (Fourth edition) RC127 Chemical Industries Associations London 2003

6   *James Reason Managing the Risks of Organizational Accidents* Ashgate Publishing Limited 1997
ISBN 1 84014 104 2

7   http://webcommunities.hse.gov.uk/ui/inovem.ti/group/chemicalindustries.pspm/grouphome

8   www.cia.org.uk/newsite/responsible_care/cells.htm

9   *Leadership for the major hazard industries* Leaflet INDG277(rev1) HSE Books 2004 (single copy free or priced packs of 15 ISBN 0 7176 2905 8)

Whilo ovory offort has been made to ensure the accuracy of the references listed in this publication, their future availability cannot be guaranteed.

Further information

HSE priced and free publications are available by mail order from HSE Books, PO Box 1999, Sudbury, Suffolk CO10 2WA Tel: 01787 881165 Fax: 01787 313995 Website: www.hsebooks.co.uk (HSE priced publications are also available from bookshops and free leaflets can be downloaded from HSE's website: www.hse.gov.uk.)

For information about health and safety ring HSE's Infoline Tel: 0845 345 0055 Fax: 0845 408 9566 Textphone: 0845 408 9577 e-mail: hse.infoline@natbrit.com or write to HSE Information Services, Caerphilly Business Park, Caerphilly CF83 3GG.

recycle When you have finished with this leaflet please recycle it

75% recycled This leaflet is printed on 75% recycled paper